I NEARLY DIED LAUGHING

Tony Husband

ARCTURUS

'Men of Tony's unique and uncompromising vision come along once every ten thousand years. They are never simply "born". They are the result of an asteroid collision in the heavens or they are found curled up in an oyster as they tread the razor's edge between myth and legend and bewildering genius. Tony himself oozed out of a phoenix. I thank Jesus I was alive in his time.'

Guy Garvey, *Elbow*

. . . .

'Tony Husband is the Keith Richards of the cartoon world.'

Dan Kieran, *The Idler*

. . . .

'Tony Husband is even funnier than I am.'

Griff Rhys Jones, comedian, writer, TV presenter

. . . .

'Gloomy, appears all over the place, but full of very funny and at times risqué cartoons about despair and marriage.'

Michael Heath, cartoonist

. . . .

'I'm a big fan of Tony's. He's been making me laugh for 25 years.'

Alan Davies, actor and comedian

'One of the few good things about being unemployed in the 1980s was waiting for a fortnightly fix of Tony Husband's *Yobs*... classic cartooning. He's a northern treasure.'

Christopher Eccleston, actor

· ·

'Tony is consistently funny and inventive. I've been a fan of his for as long as I can remember.'

John Lloyd, producer of *QI* and *Blackadder*

· ·

'Tony has great charm... in person and with his cartoons. The guy is a genius!'

Peter Hook, *Joy Division* and *New Order*

· ·

'Tony Husband is consistently one of the funniest cartoonists around.'

Michael Palin, actor, comedian, broadcaster

· ·

'Over the last 30 years, it's safe to say he's made me laugh out loud more than anybody else... he comes from a dark, twisted place.'

Marc Riley, BBC 6 Music

For Paul

The cover image and cartoons on pages 8, 9, 10, 11, 13, 14, 16, 17, 29, 30, 57, 58, 59, 68, 77, 83, 87, 89, 90, 92, 100, 106, 108, 109, 114, 116, 117, 121, 124, 131, 136, 138, 139, 142, 144, 146, 147, 149, 151, 152, 153, 157, 158 and 160 are reproduced by kind permission of *PRIVATE EYE* magazine / Tony Husband. The cartoon on page 44 appears by kind permission of *PUNCH* magazine.

ARCTURUS

This edition published in 2012 by Arcturus Publishing Limited
26/27 Bickels Yard, 151–153 Bermondsey Street,
London SE1 3HA

ISBN: 978-1-84858-123-4
AD002326EN

Printed in China

With special thanks to Annie Quigley and the cat

MY HUSBAND AND I

Of course, if you want to be a cartoonist you have to be able to draw. But it's not about drawing. Some cartoonists exhibit fine draftsmanship, almost too exquisite for the medium in fact; most stick to simple delineations and the distinctive faces and expressions peculiar to their style.

It's about the joke. But the joke isn't just a frozen tableau. Nor need it be a joke in the usual sense. The best cartoons look out at you and you look in at them, and the characters inside look at each other. And as human beings we decide whose side we're on, what's happening and where we fit into the picture. To paraphrase Karl Kraus, a cartoon is a mirror: if an ass looks in you can't expect an apostle to peep out.

Not that you notice that with the greats. And Tony Husband is one of the greats. He is not of the malevolent, vicious school. His skill with a pencil is up there with Michael Heath and Matt and Honeysett and Kipper Williams – choose a favourite. Tony, like Matt, is more benign, but what looks like a scabbard often turns out to be a sharp and unsheathed sword.

Every day he finds it somewhere in himself to frame some element of human absurdity. He observes without anger or superiority, for he is down there with his characters.

That he is a loveable, kindly man you can tell from his work. But you can also detect those great gifts he shares with the best in his field: economy, insight, intelligence and a deep humanity. You are very lucky to be holding this book. Enjoy...

Stephen Fry

'The pyramids?... No, you should have taken a left a while back there.'

'It's very nice but I think defensively the conservatory will be our weak spot.'

'How are you getting on with your neighbours these days?'

'Come in, Jeremy. Sit down.'

'Doesn't he look different on television?'

'Erm, we're just checking. You are in fancy dress, aren't you?'

'Isn't there a game we could both play, Keith?'

'Yes, we like our wine.'

'Jill, what time is my wife's funeral?'

'Michael was trying to get a western saloon look with the cat flap.'

The ~~Four~~ 3 Wise Men

'Not the most adventurous of hunters, was he?'

'I told next door he would struggle with his new hedge-cutter.'

'Phil, I think you might have got the wrong idea about this fantasy football.'

'Run, they lost again.'

'This will get the neighbours talking.'

'They are lovely, Martha... Martha?...'

'Darling, before you jump, can you find my rare collection of Beatles singles?'

'That's a tough school. The uniform is body armour.'

'Erm... I didn't mean for you to push that hard.'

'You spoil that goldfish.'

'If you want my body and you think I'm sexy...'

'What girl in the cake?'

'Sorry, won't be a minute.'

'I know you love trifle, Roger, but so does everybody else.'

'Let he who is without sin cast the first stone.'

'Thanks... I don't normally accept drinks off ugly men but I'm skint.'

'Don't make me do anything you might regret, young man.'

'Money is short, okay?!!'

'Congratulations on your promotion. It's a creeper.'

'We met through our involvement in care in the community.'

'This is amazing. It seems the female gorilla is knitting me a cardigan.'

'I think my husband suspects.'

Oh yes, the best days of my life were spent playing rugby.

'I sometimes wish you had another job.'

'Don't worry, he always feigns death when it's his round.'

'You need to see a doctor about your condition, Roger.'

'...and they're destroying the countryside.'

'They seem a bit strict with their kids.'

'Why don't you get the train to work like everybody else?'

'Yes, it's a pretty rough area... Morning, vicar.'

'Hi, Mum. It's bad news: he's got the all clear.'

'For God's sake slow down, Wilson, speed camera!'

'Hopefully, we'll have a quiet night tonight.'

'Mum, Dad, what do you mean I'm adopted?!!'

'Well, it doesn't look much like voluntary euthanasia to me, Mrs Hill.'

'I knew I was right. "The ankle bone's connected to the leg bone, the leg bone's connected to the..."'

'I quite like sex, but you're not too keen, are you, dear?'

'Don't worry it's an old sign.'

'A quick one, James: did you get that contract signed for the new client?'

'I wouldn't normally come out on Christmas Eve.'

'Ten-nine-eight-seven...'

'Stop whingeing, Wilson, we all have to start somewhere.'

'I want to complain about the way you've lifted my bottom.'

'Oh, wow! She can test my eyes any time.'

'Tch... his idea of foreplay is to take his socks off.'

Christmas at the Frankensteins'

'Shall I sign it in joined-up writing?'

'Sex?! It's not your birthday.'

'Listen, dear, his first word.'

'For goodness sake, Martin, it's only a couple of slugs.'

'I'm not booking you, I just want your autograph.'

'You should involve your wife more in golf
like I did, Martin... Come on, dear, keep up.'

'Amazing, you've gone back into your family
400 years and they're all as boring as you.'

'He was an optician.'

'I don't think stamping on it will do much good.'

'Mummy, I think grandad might have fallen in the tank with the piranhas.'

'Why can't you just go for a swim like everybody else?'

'Right... do you find me a/. very sexy b/. sexy c/. not sexy at all?'

'George, what exactly did you say in your letter to the Prime Minister?'

'Well, I don't call it heaven when we're not allowed to sniff each other's bottom.'

'We've bought ourselves a little property abroad.'

'Oi, I've just painted that.'

'The rumour is the new MD's a bit of a ruthless bastard.'

'Oh, excuse me, I've just had a text.'

'Mark, perhaps Karen and Stewart don't want to see your piles.'

'You want to marry me, Norman, oh my gosh, are you sure?!!'

'Of course, we're pleased you've taken up tennis, son, it's just...'

'I told you not to shout abuse.'

'I think he's swallowed the mobile phone.'

'Throw it back?!!... I can't.'

'He's in the garden catching moles.'

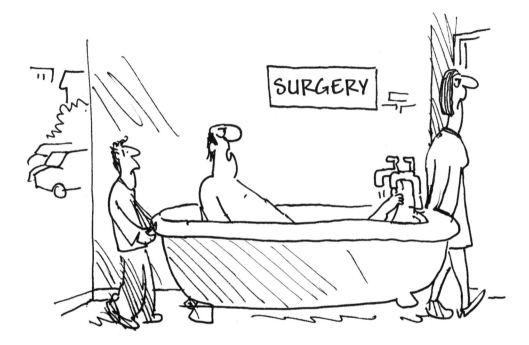

'I don't see why the doctor couldn't have come out.'

'This is supposed to be the longest escalator in the world.'

'We're looking for a thief who smells nice.
She got him with her perfume not her mace.'

'My garden is so big I need a lawnmower with satnav.'

'Apparently, he believed in reincarnation.'

'I sometimes think you're being too cautious with the children.'

'Have him checked for drugs.'

'I think there might be something in this global warming theory, Derek.'

'It was Barbara's last wish... we invite our best friends round and eat her.'

'OK, Tim, Mrs Booth is here for your piano lesson.
Where have you hidden the piano?'

'With all the foreigners in the team, we rely on sign language.'

'Can you take me somewhere I can smoke?'

'He beats one man, he beats another...
the police are pulling him off a third man.'

'Okay, Mr Noble, your results are back.'

'Isn't that the breed whose parents are fiercely protective?'

'Mr Smith isn't in at the moment, but he's asked me to tell you you're fired.'

'What?'

'Your dog's worrying my sheep.'

'They're playing havoc with my wind chimes.'

'George, do you mind if we leave out the puppet show tonight? I'm tired.'

'Did I hear you say this was your first christening?'

'Don't be deceived by Dennis. He's a titan in bed.'

'We're not going to see any dolphins with him around.'

'I killed my wife and buried her in the garden today... Does that make me a bad person, Joe?'

'Father, I'm having wicked thoughts.'

'Ah, Jones, the end-of-year individual sales figures are in.'

'Harvey, have you electrified the birdbath again?'

'It's taking Patrick longer than he thought to get his singled–handed,
round–the–world yacht race out of his system.'

'We'd better do as he says.'

'Erm... I think we've had enough sex for one marriage, don't you, Peter?'

'Pictures coming back from Mars show a bleak desolate landscape...'

'Hoodies! Form a circle.'

'I love coming the quiet route across the Alps.'

'Cash? Ta, mate, that'll do nicely.'

'Brian's trying to grow a beard.'

'Blimey, is that the time already?'

'Looks like Hobson's got the push.'

'They're an old boy band.'

'Aren't you supposed to take your trousers off?'

'Your Tom is very much like his father, isn't he?'

'He's having trouble with his motions.'

'He's trying to tell me something.'

'You can't fool me, Eric. The bird's died, hasn't it?'

'So he is watering down the beer.'

'The keeper's having a quiet game.'

'Bad day at the office, dear?'

'It's the nursing home. Grandad's done his back breakdancing again.'

'I think he's still hungry.'

'You're supposed to keep an eye on the clients, Emily.'

'I want to be a foreign player when I grow up.'

'Hello, I'm Ronald. I impersonate people.'

'It's for you.'

'Just a minute... You're not my wife.'

'I'm retiring soon, Marcus, and I'm looking for someone to take over.'

'He's got your halo.'

'What's got into the sheep?'